# Horizons

# Phonics and Reading

# 1

## Workbook Two

**Author:**

*Polly A. Wood, M.A.*

**Editor:**

*Alan Christopherson, M.S.*

**Graphic Design:**

*JoAnn Cumming*

**Illustration:**

*Alpha Omega Creative Services*

Alpha Omega Publications, Inc. • Rock Rapids, IA

Horizons Phonics and Reading 1, Workbook Two

© MMI by Alpha Omega Publications, Inc.®
804 N. 2nd Ave. E., Rock Rapids, IA 51246-1759

*Printed in the United States of America*

ISBN 978-0-7403-0318-0

**Rule:**

The prefix *re-* usually means *to do again*.
Examples: *reread* = to read again; *repack* = to pack again.

**1** Add the prefix *re-* to the base words. Write the new words on the lines.

do

read

make

write

load

tie

**2** Draw lines to match the words with their meanings.

| | |
|---|---|
| remake | to write again |
| redo | to load again |
| rewrite | to tie again |
| retie | to wind again |
| reload | to do again |
| rewind | to make again |

**3** **Read each sentence. Use the words from the list to complete the sentences.**

## Word List

| remake | redo | rewrite | retie | reload | rewind |
|---|---|---|---|---|---|

1. Jacob had to _____ his bed.

2. Joan needed to _____ her shoes.

3. Please _____ the clock.

4. I will _____ my letter to my grandma.

**4** **Draw lines to match the words with the pictures.**

remake

rewrite

retie

rewind

Prefix un-

Name: _____

## Rule:

The prefix *un-* usually means the *opposite* of the original word.
Examples: *unbutton*, *unlock*.

 **1** Add the prefix *un-* to the base words. Write the new words on the lines.

lock _____          happy _____

load _____          dress _____

usual _____          wrap _____

buckle _____          likely _____

tie _____

**2** Draw lines to match the words with their meanings.

opposite of wrap

not likely

opposite of do

opposite of pack

unlock
untie
unwrap
unhappy
unusual
unlikely
unsafe
undo
unpack

opposite of lock

opposite of tie

not safe

not usual

not happy

# 3

**Read each sentence. Use the words from the list to complete the sentences. Write the words on the lines.**

## Word List

| unwrap | unhappy | unpack | unsafe |
|---|---|---|---|

1. Jason had to _____ the boxes.

2. It is _____ to ride your bike after dark.

3. Jane was _____ when she had to go inside.

4. Bob had lots of presents to _____ .

# 4

**Draw lines to match the pictures to the words.**

unhappy

unpack

unlock

untie

unwrap

**5** Write two sentences using words from the word list.

## Word List

| unhappy | unpack | unlock | untie | unwrap |
| --- | --- | --- | --- | --- |

1. _____

_____

_____

2. _____

_____

_____

**Look at the pictures. Finish the words under each picture with the prefix un-. Then read the words to your teacher.**

_____ wrap

_____ happy

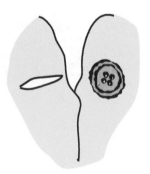

_____ button

_____ safe

_____ tied

_____ load

_____ lock

_____ pack

_____ wind

## Rule Review:

**The prefix** *re-* **usually means** *to do again*.
**The prefix** *un-* **usually means the** *opposite* **of the original word.**

**Read the story.  Use the words from the list to complete the story.**

## Word List

| reread | redo | rewinds | remake | repacks | retie |

Mark has a list of things that he has to do every day.

If he doesn't do things correctly, he has to _____

them. When he gets up, he has to _____ his bed.

He sometimes _____ his clock. He doesn't want

to have to _____ his shoes, so he does it right

the first time. He also _____ his backpack for

school. He likes to _____ the same book every

night before he goes to bed.

**2** Draw lines to match the pictures to the words.

reread

rewrite

repack

unload

**3** Use the words from the list to complete the crossword puzzle.

unwind        unload        untie        unlock

**ACROSS:**
1. The opposite of load

**DOWN:**
2. The opposite of tie
3. The opposite of lock
4. The opposite of wind

**4** **Add the prefixes _un-_ or _re-_ to the base words. Write the new words on the lines.**

1. She had to _____ the door to get in the house.
   lock

2. I need to _____ my shoes so that I don't trip.
   tie

3. I don't want to be _____ when I play a game.
   fair

4. I have to _____ my homework because I didn't
   do
   do my best.

5. Please _____ your letter to Grandma.
   write

6. He will _____ his birthday presents.
   wrap

**Draw a line to match the word with its meaning.**

| | |
|---|---|
| reread | to load again |
| rewrite | the opposite of wind |
| repack | to pack again |
| unload | the opposite of load |
| unwind | to write again |
| reload | the opposite of lock |
| untie | to read again |
| unlock | the opposite of tie |

## Rule:

The prefix dis- also means the opposite of the original word. Examples: disobey, displeased.

✏️ **Add the prefix dis- to the base words. Write the new words on the lines.**

obey _____

agree _____

order _____

grace _____

color _____

trust _____

like _____

appear _____

## 2. Draw lines to match the words with their meanings.

distrust                not in order

disorder                opposite of connect

dislike                 to not obey

disagree                to not trust

disconnect              to not like

disobey                 to not agree

## 3. Read each sentence. Use some of the words from above to complete the sentences.

1. It is not good to _____ your parents.

2. I _____ rainy days.

3. The room was in _____,
   and needed to be cleaned up.

4. It is all right to _____ with someone,
   as long as you are polite.

## Rule Review:

The prefix *re-* usually means *to do again*.
The prefixes *un-* and *dis-* usually mean the *opposite* of the original word.

**1** Add the prefixes *re-*, *un-*, or *dis-* to the base words.  Write the new words on the lines. Some of them may have two answers.

agree       _____

obey        _____

trust       _____

lock        _____

pay         _____

appear      _____

**2** Add the prefix *re-* to each of the words below, then read the words to your teacher.

_____ play        _____ write        _____ pack

_____ do          _____ load         _____ read

**3** Read each word. Use the words from the list to find opposites.
Write the opposite words on the lines.

## Word List

| undo | unhappy | disagree | disappear | disobey |

appear _____

obey _____

agree _____

do _____

happy _____

**4** Use the words from the list to finish the sentences.

## Word List

| unsafe | disappear | disagree | unwrap |

1. When you get a gift, you _____ it.

2. When things go away, they _____ .

3. When you _____ with someone, be polite.

4. Never skate on _____ ice.

## Rule:

In a consonant blend, two or more consonants come together in a word.
Their sounds blend together, but each sound is heard. Examples: _green_, _frog_, _tree_, _drip_, _bride_.

  Say the name of each picture.  Print the beginning _r_ blend on the line.

_____ip          _____ain          _____og

_____apes        _____ess          _____ee

_____ide         _____ay           _____um

**2** **Read each word and look at the pictures.**
**Color the pictures with *tr* blends brown. Color the pictures with *gr* blends green.**
**Color the pictures with *dr* blends red. Color the pictures with *fr* blends blue.**

frog

tree

dress

grass

fruit

drum

**3** **Draw lines to match the pictures with the words.**

fruit

drive

train

press

brick

Checkup:
Beginning Consonant
Blends with l

Name: _____

## Rule:

In a consonant blend with *l*, two or more consonants come together in a word.
Their sounds blend together, but each sound is heard. Examples: *black*, *plant*, *sled*.

**1.** For each word, find a word from the list with the same *l* blend. Write the words on the lines.

### Word List

| block | clean | glass | fly | play | slide |
|-------|-------|-------|-----|------|-------|

clock _____

black _____

flat _____

glad _____

plant _____

sled _____

**2.** Draw lines to match the pictures with the words.

glue

play

clouds

sled

blocks

fly

## 3  Add the correct l blend to the beginning of each word. Check your work using the words from the list

### Word List

| please | blocks | close | blue | blow |
|--------|--------|-------|------|------|

_____ocks

_____ue

_____ose

_____ow

_____ease

## 4  Read each word.
Color the pictures that begin with **bl** brown. Color the pictures that begin with **pl** red. Color the pictures that begin with **gl** green. Color the pictures that begin with **fl** blue. Color the pictures that begin with **sl** orange.

glue

sled

flag

flowers

blocks

plane

## Rule Review:

In an ending consonant blend, two or more consonants come together at the end of a word. Their sounds blend together, but each sound is heard.

**1.** Read each sentence. Underline the word that completes the sentence. Write the word on the line.

1. I will study hard for my math _____.

   rest          test

2. I drank _____ a glass of milk.

   half        shelf

3. A camel has a big _____ on his back.

   lamp          hump

4. I will _____ my teacher for help.

   ask          risk

5. I write with my _____ hand.

   lift        left

**2.** Draw lines to match the pictures with the words. Circle the ending consonant blend in each word.

rest

plant

child

lamp

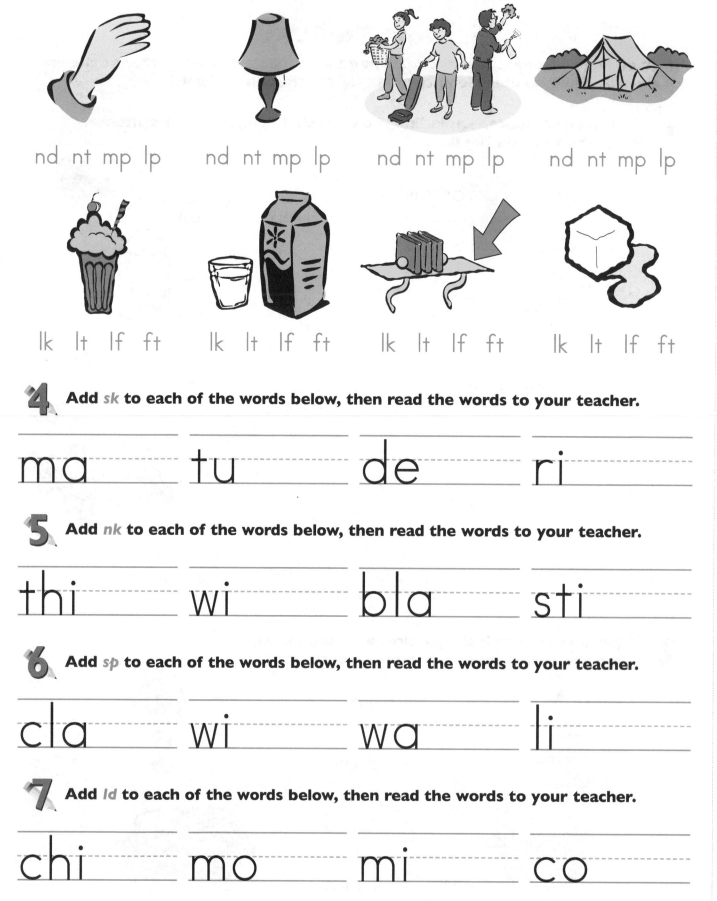

**3** Look at the pictures.
Circle the consonant blend that makes the ending sound you hear.

nd  nt  mp  lp          nd  nt  mp  lp          nd  nt  mp  lp          nd  nt  mp  lp

lk  lt  lf  ft          lk  lt  lf  ft          lk  lt  lf  ft          lk  lt  lf  ft

**4** Add *sk* to each of the words below, then read the words to your teacher.

ma          tu          de          ri

**5** Add *nk* to each of the words below, then read the words to your teacher.

thi          wi          bla          sti

**6** Add *sp* to each of the words below, then read the words to your teacher.

cla          wi          wa          li

**7** Add *ld* to each of the words below, then read the words to your teacher.

chi          mo          mi          co

## Lesson 89

Writing Lesson:
Personal Narrative

Name: _____

_____

**Personal Narrative – On a separate sheet of paper, write a narrative about a fun time that you have had.**

Your story can be about a fun vacation or any other fun time you had with family or friends. Have your teacher or writing partner help you write your narrative. Remember to tell what you did, where and when you did it, and why it was fun. Also remember to use capital letters at the beginnings of sentences, for people's names, and other places where they are needed.

When you are finished writing, have your partner or teacher help you find any mistakes or places where you might need to rewrite. Then write your final copy on the lines on the back of this page.

## Rule:

In a consonant blend with _s_, two or more consonants come together in a word.  Their sounds blend together, but each sound is heard.  **Examples:** _spell_, _snail_, _string_, _skip_, _swing_.

**1.** Draw lines to match the pictures with the words.

swing

sky

stamp

street

snail

spoon

**2.** Complete each word with an _s_ blend.  Use the words from above. Read the words to your teacher.

amp          ing          ail

y          oon          eet

**3** **Read each sentence. Underline the word that completes the sentence. Write the word on the line.**

1. John went on a camping trip last _____ with his mom and dad.

   spring     spot

2. It was _____ cold.

   still     stop

3. Everyone wore _____.

   stamp     sweaters

4. They _____ three days in the forest.

   spent     sport

5. John saw a _____.

   spray     snake

6. He _____ when he saw it.

   swept     screamed

7. Then it _____ away.

   stood     slithered

**4** **Look at the pictures below. Circle the correct s blend for each word.**

sp  sn  str  sk          sw  sp  sn  str          sk  sw  sp  sn          str  sk  sw  sp

**1.** **Add the prefix** *re-*, *un-*, **or** *dis-* **to the base words.**
**Some of the words may use two prefixes.**

_____read

_____happy

_____obey

_____write

_____safe

_____pleased

_____lock

_____appear

_____do

_____order

_____lock

_____appear

_____do

_____order

**2.** **Look at each picture. Circle the correct consonant blend.**

br  dr  fr  pr  tr       br  dr  fr  pr  tr       cl  fl  gl  bl  pl       cl  fl  gl  bl  pl

sk  sn  sp  str  sw       sk  sn  sp  str  sw       br  bl  dr  pr  pl       cr  cl  fr  fl  gr

**3** **Read each sentence.  Add the correct prefix to the base word and write the new word on the line.**

1. Shawn is _____ about losing his toy.
   happy

2. It is _____ to ride your bike at night without a light.
   safe

3. Dad needed to _____ his letter.
   write

4. _____ the door with the key.
   lock

5. The magician made the rabbit _____.
   appear

6. She has to _____ her homework.
   do

**4** **Draw lines to match the words with the definitions.**

| to heat again | replay |
| to wind again | unpack |
| opposite of pack | rewind |
| to play again | reheat |

## Rule:

Sometimes y at the end of a word can make the long ē or long ī sound.

 **Draw lines to match the pictures with the words.**

penny

bunny

fly

baby

happy

cry

puppy

**2** Read the story. Underline all of the words that end in y.
Put the words into the correct categories.

Molly was taking care of baby Tommy. She heard him cry in his crib. He was not happy. She had to try everything to calm him down. She read him a silly book about dogs that fly. Finally, he was better.

| Y = long ē |
| --- |
|  |

| Y = long ī |
| --- |
|  |

**3** Read each sentence.  Underline the word that completes each sentence. Write the word on the line.

1. The _____ was cloudy.
   sky    sly

2. The day was _____ .
   rocky    rainy

3. We stayed inside to stay _____ .
   very    dry

4. Mom wanted us to _____ to have fun.
   try    my

5. I felt _____ .
   fry    sleepy

**4** Use the words from the list to name the pictures. Write the words on the lines.

_____

_____

_____

_____

_____

_____

fry

sunny

celery

fly

bunny

cherry

**5** **Read each riddle.  Unscramble the word that answers each riddle.**

1. This animal is furry and hops.

nnyub

2. If there are no clouds in the sky,
   it is this kind of day.

ynuns

3. If you did something that you wish
   you hadn't done, you might be this.

oyrrs

4. When you ask a question, you

hyw

5. After it rains, dirt often gets this way.

ddyum

30

## Rule:

A consonant digraph is two or more consonants that stay together to make their special sound. Examples: *the*, *that*, *three*.

**1** Look at the pictures. Circle the pictures whose names start with *th*.

 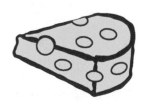

**2** Add *th* to the beginning of each word, then read the words to your teacher.

umb      ree      en

at      ese      is

irteen      ick      ey

th th th th th th th th th

**3** Look at each picture. Write the word that names each picture. Write the word on the line.

## Word List

| thick | thorn | teeth | thin |
|-------|-------|-------|------|

_____

_____

_____

_____

**4** Read each sentence. Underline the correct word to complete each sentence. Write the word on the line.

1. In the morning, we brush our _____ .

truck      teeth

2. Mike's brother is _____ years old.

three      then

3. _____ are our friends.

This      They

4. _____ is my house.

Then      This

## Rule:

A consonant digraph is two consonants that stay together to make their special sound. Consonant digraph *tch* makes the sound you hear in *kitchen*, *watch*, and *stitch*.

**1** **Look at the pictures.  Circle the pictures whose names contain *tch*.**

**2** **Add *tch* to each of the words below, then read the words to your teacher.**

wa _____     ki _____ en     ca _____     pi _____ er

fe _____     ma _____     swi _____     sti _____

**3** **Read each sentence. Use the words from the list to complete each sentence. Write the word on the line.**

## Word List

| match | watch | batch | kitchen | catch |
|-------|-------|-------|---------|-------|

1. I use a _____ to tell time.

2. We eat our meals in the _____ .

3. I like to _____ the ball when it is thrown to me.

4. Most of my socks _____ .

5. Mom made a _____ of cookies.

**4** **Unscramble the words. Use the words from the list to help you.**

## Word List

| kitchen | stitch | match | itch | watch | switch |
|---------|--------|-------|------|-------|--------|

enikcht _____     amcht _____

tithcs _____     ciht _____

wahct _____     wistch _____

## Rule:
A consonant digraph is two or more consonants that stay together to make their special sound. Examples: *thick*, *match*, *this*.

**1** Look at the pictures. Circle the pictures whose names contain either *th* or *tch*.

**2** Draw lines to match the pictures with the words.

thirteen

watch

13

kitchen

thumb

**3** Use the words from the list to complete the crossword puzzle.

think

this

nothing

kitchen

**ACROSS:**

1. _____ is my house.

3. Mom makes dinner in the
   _____ .

**DOWN:**

2. You need to _____ when
   you do your homework.

4. There was _____ to do
   on a rainy day.

**4** Write three sentences, using at least six of the words from this lesson.

1. _____

2. _____

3. _____

## Rule:

A consonant digraph is two or more consonants that stay together to make their special sound. Examples: *shoe*, *show*, *shirt*.

**1** Look at the pictures. Circle the pictures whose names begin with *sh*.

**2** Add *sh* to each of the words below, then read the words to your teacher.

_____ oe        _____ ine    bru _____     fi _____

a _____    es        _____ op        _____ ip        _____ ut

**3** Look at the pictures below. Circle the *sh* to show whether the *sh* sound is at the beginning or at the end of the word.

  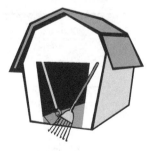    

sh        sh    sh        sh    sh        sh    sh        sh

**Look at the pictures. Write the names of the pictures. Use the list to help you.**

### Word List

| dish | fish | shell | brush | shin | shoe |

_____

_____

_____

_____

_____

_____

**Read each sentence. Use the words from above to complete each sentence. Write the words on the lines.**

1. Henry has three kinds of _____ in his tank.

2. I found a _____ on the beach.

3. I have a scrape on my _____ .

4. John ate his food off a _____ .

5. She uses a _____ for her hair.

## Rule:

A consonant digraph is two or more consonants that stay together to make their special sound. Consonant digraph *ch* can be used at the beginning or end of a word. Examples: _chin_, _such_, _sandwich_.

**1** Look at the pictures. Circle the pictures whose names contain *ch*.

**2** Draw lines to match the pictures with the words.

beach

chimp

chair

peach

chop

**3** Add *ch* to each of the words below, then read the words to your teacher.

air          in pea          mu

est          urn          ill          op

pun          crun          bran          unk

pin          su          whi          ri

ums          eese          ips          at

**4** Write three sentences using at least six of the words from this lesson.

1.

2.

3.

## Rule Review:

**A consonant digraph is two or more consonants put together that make one sound.**

**1** **Read the story. Underline the words that contain *sh* or *ch*. Put the words into the correct categories.**

Mary had fun at the circus. She saw many things there, but the clowns were her favorite. They each had different funny acts. They all put on a really good show. Some of them had big shoes. They all had funny, painted faces. Mary laughed so much, she didn't want to go home.

| sh |
| --- |

| ch |
| --- |

**2** **Draw lines to match the pictures with the words.**

chin

cherry

dish

shoe

chair

chick

**3** Read each sentence. Use the words from the list to complete each sentence. Write the word on the line.

## Word List

chin      cherry      dish      shoe      chair      chick

1. I like _____ pie.

2. She sat in her favorite _____.

3. The dog drinks water from his _____.

4. The hen had a baby _____.

5. I have a hole in my _____.

**4** Use the words from the list to complete the crossword puzzle.

cheese      hush      shirt      sandwich      chair

**ACROSS:**
1. This is what we can sit in.
3. You might have one of these for lunch.
4. This can have long or short sleeves.

**DOWN:**
2. Mice might like this.
5. If you are too noisy, you might be told to do this.

**Writing a Report – Write a report about an animal.**

You are going to write a report about an animal. A report tells the reader information about something. Only facts, or things that can be proven to be true, are written in a report. Have your teacher or writing partner help you find information about an animal on which you want to do your report. Pick out at least five facts about the animal. Your teacher or partner can help you write them down. Then decide what order to put them in.

Write your first copy on a piece of paper. Have your teacher or partner help you check for any mistakes, then write your final copy in your book.

**My Report About** _____

## Rule:

A compound word is a word made from two or more words joined together to make one word. Examples: *backyard*, *runway*, *mailbox*.

**Read each compound word. Break each compound word into two words. Write the words on the lines.**

backyard

mailbox

peanut

pancake

cupcake

raincoat

popcorn

sandbox

backpack

sailboat

**2** Draw lines to match the words with their meanings.

| | |
|---|---|
| mailbox | a coat for rain |
| raincoat | corn that can pop |
| sandbox | cake in a cup |
| cupcake | a pack for your back |
| backpack | box with sand |
| popcorn | box for mail |

**3** Word Search – Use the words from the list.  The words go across or up and down.

| seaweed | railroad | oatmeal | myself |
|---|---|---|---|
| baseball | classroom | maybe | cupcake |

```
s  c  m  y  s  e  l  f  r
e  u  p  o  e  r  o  o  a
a  p  l  u  l  r  a  r  i
w  c  o  i  e  a  t  m  l
e  a  t  e  r  a  m  a  r
e  k  e  z  o  t  e  r  o
d  e  a  n  u  f  a  m  a
b  a  s  e  b  a  l  l  d
c  l  a  s  s  r  o  o  m
m  a  y  b  e  e  t  e  d
```

## Rules:

A *base word* is a word without a prefix or a suffix added to it.
A prefix is a beginning that is added to a base word to change its meaning.
**Examples:** *do = redo, dress = undress, obey = disobey.*
A suffix is an ending that is added to a base word to change its meaning.
**Examples:** *jump = jumped, start = starting, climb = climbing.*

**Read each word. Divide each word into its** *prefix,* *base word,* **and** *suffix.*
**Some of the words will have both a prefix and a suffix.**

unlike _____   _____   _____

rereading _____   _____   _____

jumping _____   _____   _____

trying _____   _____   _____

unwinding _____   _____   _____

redoing _____   _____   _____

**2** **Read each sentence. Add the correct prefix or suffix to the base word.**
**Write the word on the line.**

1. Nancy is going to _____ her homework
   do

2. Our house is _____ any other house on our
   like
   street.

3. My sister is _____ rope.
   jump

4. I am _____ to do my best.
   try

5. This book was so good that I am _____ it.
   read

**3** **Use the words from the list to answer the riddles.**

### Word List

| sleepless | useless | playful | careful |
|-----------|---------|---------|---------|

1. You must be _____ when riding your bike.

2. A new puppy usually acts _____ .

3. A broken light bulb is _____ .

4. If you didn't get any sleep, you are _____ .

# Test 10
Lessons 91–100
23 points

Name: _____

**1.** Read each word. Put the words into the correct categories.

## Word List

| fly | by | city | why | my | every | safely | money |

Y = long ī                    Y = long ē

_____        _____

_____        _____

_____        _____

_____        _____

_____        _____

**2.** Read each compound word. Break each compound word into two words. Write the words on the lines.

playground    _____    _____

mailbox       _____    _____

daylight      _____    _____

nightgown     _____    _____

peanut        _____    _____

**3** Read each sentence. Use the words from the list to complete each sentence. Write the word on the line.

## Word List

| shame | match | chair | shoes | touch |
|-------|-------|-------|-------|-------|

1. Jack is wearing socks that _____.

2. Please don't _____ the hot stove.

3. Mary needs a new pair of _____.

4. That is my favorite _____ to sit in.

5. It is a _____ that our team didn't win the game.

**4** Separate each word into its prefix, base word, and suffix.

replaying _____ _____ _____

undoing _____ _____ _____

unsafely _____ _____ _____

disobeying _____ _____ _____

unkindly _____ _____ _____

## Rule:

**A prefix is always a separate syllable in a word.**

**1.** **Read each word.  Divide the words into syllables.  Use a hyphen (-) to divide the word.**

unsafe _____     renew _____

retell _____     rewrite _____

unpaid _____     dislike _____

unkind _____     unwise _____

**2.** **Read each sentence.  Underline the word from each sentence that contains a prefix.  Write the word on the line.  Use a hyphen to divide the word into syllables.**

1. Sam was being unsafe.     _____

2. It was time to unload the car.     _____

3. I dislike that color.     _____

4. Please don't be unkind.     _____

5. We need to repaint our house.     _____

**3** **Draw lines to match the pictures with the words.**

unwind

rebuild

replay

repaint

**4** **Read each sentence. Use the words from the list to complete each sentence. Write the word on the line.**

## Word List

| unkind | unwise | unpaid | untied | rewrite |

1. It is _____ to disobey your parents.

2. I have to _____ my letter.

3. This bill is still _____ .

4. The dog _____ my shoe.

5. Don't be _____ to your friends.

## Rule:

**A suffix is a syllable if it contains a vowel sound.**

1. **Read each word. Divide the words into syllables. Use a hyphen to divide each word.**

colder

spoonful

careful

harmless

softly

building

playing

careless

reading

softness

**2** **Draw lines to match the words with the pictures.**

spoonful

planted

playing

flying

**3** **Read each sentence. Use the words from above to complete each sentence. Write the word on the line.**

## Word List

spoonful     planted     careless     playing     flying

1. Nancy took a _____ of medicine.

2. We _____ the flowers.

3. The birds are _____ south for the winter.

4. The children are _____ at recess.

5. Don't be _____ when
you play on the slide.

# Lesson 103

**Syllables: Compound Words**

Name: _____

## Rule:

A **compound word** is divided between the words that make up the compound word.

✎ Divide each compound word into syllables. Write each word on the line. Use a hyphen to divide each word.

into _____

birthday _____

today _____

rainbow _____

hillside _____

bedtime _____

inside _____

outside _____

cowboy _____

tonight _____

**Use the words from the list to complete the crossword puzzle.**

today        tiptoe        bedtime        dustpan        Pancakes

**ACROSS:**

1. When you want to walk quietly, you should _____ .

3. Sweep the dirt into a _____ .

5. My _____ is 8:30 p.m.

**DOWN:**

2. This day is called _____ .

4. _____ are good to eat for breakfast.

## Lesson 104

**Review:**
Prefixes, Suffixes,
Compound Words, Syllables

Name: _____

## Rule Review:

A prefix is always a separate syllable in a word. A suffix is a syllable if it contains a vowel sound. A compound word is divided between the words that make up the compound word.

**Divide the words into syllables. Write the words on the lines. Use a hyphen to divide the words.**

repaint _____

unkind _____

building _____

inside _____

someone _____

bedtime _____

cowboy _____

dislike _____

spoonful _____

unload _____

*Horizons Phonics & Reading 1, Workbook Two*

57

**2** **Read each sentence. Use the words from the word list to complete each sentence. Write the word on the line.**

## Word List

inside    someone    redo    cowboy    dislike    building

1. She is _____ I know.

2. We have to stay _____ when it is raining.

3. I _____ the taste of that medicine.

4. The _____ was riding a horse.

5. They are _____ a new house.

6. I messed up my picture, so I will _____ it.

You write a thank you note to someone after they have given you a gift or have done something especially nice for you. Thank you notes are similar to friendly letters. They have a date, greeting, body, closing and signature.

In a thank you note, you thank the person for what he or she has given to you or has done for you. Here is an example of a thank you note:

September 13, 20—

Dear Grandma,

Thank you for the pretty dress. I don't have anything else like it. I can wear it to school and to church. I can also wear it to birthday parties and out to dinner.

Thanks again. It was nice of you to remember me on my birthday.

Love,

Nancy

## Write a thank you note.

Think of a gift you have gotten or a nice thing that was done for you. Write a thank you note to the person who got you the gift or did the nice thing. Be sure that you name the gift or the deed and tell why it was special to you. Have your teacher or your writing partner help you write your note. Then have that person help you fix any mistakes. Write your note on a piece of paper. Then write your final copy in your book. You may mail your note if you wish.

*Horizons Phonics & Reading 1, Workbook Two*

## Definition:

**Synonyms are words that mean the same or almost the same thing but are spelled differently. Examples:** *big*/*large*, *small*/*little*, *closes*/*shuts*.

✏ **Read each word. Find its synonym in the list. Write the word on the line.**

happy _____

quiet _____

woods _____

beautiful _____

unhappy _____

finds _____

gift _____

fall _____

part _____

quick _____

**Word List**

present

glad

discovers

piece

fast

sad

drop

forest

pretty

silent

**2** **Read each sentence. Underline the word that completes each sentence. Write the word on the line.**

1. Many kinds of animals live here in the _____ .

                                   forest      farther

2. You might get a _____ for your birthday.

                  piece      present

3. You may feel _____ when something bad happens.

                sad       pretty

4. It is fun to ride your bike _____ .

                fast      sound

5. You might feel _____ when something good happens.

                tall      glad

**3** **Read each sentence. Underline the word that completes each sentence. Write the word on the line.**

1. Gail was sick, so she had to _____ home.

                take      stay

2. The _____ was sailing across the ocean.

        ship      same

3. The building was very _____ .

              took      tall

4. Deer live in the _____ .

        forest      farther

5. At night it was _____ outside.

        sound      silent

**Write four sentences.  Use at least eight words from this lesson.**

## Word List

| present | piece | drop | silent | ship | tall |
| glad | fast | forest | take | same | farther |
| discovers | sad | pretty | stay | took | sound |

1. _____

2. _____

3. _____

4. _____

**5** **Use the words from the list to complete the crossword puzzle.**

present　　forest　　pretty　　silent　　discover　　fast　　sound

**ACROSS:**

1. A synonym for noise.
5. A synonym for quiet.
6. A synonym for gift.

**DOWN:**

2. A synonym for find.
3. A synonym for woods.
4. A synonym for quick.
6. A synonym for beautiful.

*Horizons Phonics & Reading 1, Workbook Two*

Antonyms

Name:

## Definition:

Antonyms are words that are the opposite or almost the opposite in meaning.
Examples: *big/small*, *come/go*, *over/under*.

**1.** Draw lines to match the words with their antonyms.

noisy

asleep

young

hard

under

thin

loose

weak

dark

few

awake

over

fat

strong

light

many

quiet

old

soft

tight

**2.** Draw lines to match the pictures with the words.

sharp

asleep

dark

old

cold

**3** Use the list to fill in the blanks.

1. The opposite of large is _____ .

2. The opposite of slow is _____ .

3. The opposite of hard is _____ .

4. The opposite of over is _____ .

5. The opposite of hot is _____ .

**4** Write four sentences.
Use at least eight words from the lesson word list.

1. _____
_____

2. _____
_____

3. _____
_____

4. _____
_____

Homonyms

Name:

## Definition:

Homonyms are words that sound the same but have different spellings and different meanings.  Examples:  *beet*/*beat*, *weak*/*week*, *buy*/*by*.

 **Draw lines to match the homonyms..**

| | |
|---|---|
| sent | cent |
| blew | be |
| made | eight |
| road | fare |
| wait | sale |
| bee | one |
| knot | I |
| ate | blue |
| fair | write |
| won | maid |
| right | rode |
| sail | weight |
| eye | not |

## 2 Use the words from the list to complete the crossword puzzle.

write

not

pane

wrap

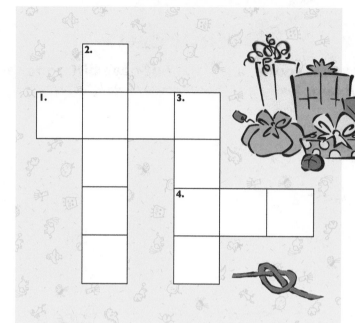

**ACROSS:**
1. Homonym for rap.
4. Homonym for knot.

**DOWN:**
2. Homonym for right.
3. Homonym for pain.

## Word List

| | | | | | |
|---|---|---|---|---|---|
| sent | made | wait | knot | fair | sail | write |
| cent | maid | weight | not | fare | sale | right |
| blew | road | be | ate | one | I | wrap |
| blue | rode | bee | eight | won | eye | rap |

## 3 Write three sentences. Use at least six of the homonyms from the word list above.

1. _____

2. _____

3. _____

## Definition Review:

*Synonyms* are words that mean the same or almost the same thing but are spelled differently.
*Antonyms* are words that are the opposite or almost the opposite in meaning.
*Homonyms* are words that sound the same but have different spellings and different meanings.

Read each sentence. Underline the correct homonym or antonym.
Write the word on the line.

1. _____ like to swim.
   Eye        I

2. The boat _____ on the water.
   sales     sails

3. I can't go _____ now.
   right     write

4. My friend _____ a lot about sailboats.
   knows     nose

5. We drove _____ the river on the bridge.
   over      under

6. We were _____ when we got to go to the zoo.
   sad       happy

**2** Read the story.
Use the correct words from the list to answer the questions after the story.

## Word List

| beat | beet | knew | new | road | rode | one | won |

John's soccer team beat most of the other teams in the league. They made it to the finals. They rode to the game in a bus. They wore their new shirts to the game. The other team was good, but John's team won the game by one point.

1. John's team _____ most of the other teams in the league.

2. They _____ to the game in a bus.

3. They wore their _____ shirts to the game.

4. John's team _____ the big game.

**3** Draw lines to match the pictures with the words.

ring

sea

beet

knot

eight

Writing Lesson:
Personal Experience
Narrative

Name:

 **Write a personal experience narrative.**

In this lesson you will be writing another personal experience narrative in which you tell about something that you have done or something that really happened to you.

You will be writing about something you do that is special. Do you take music or dance lessons? Do you take care of a pet or help around the house in some way? Those are some ideas. Maybe you can think of something else that you do that is special.

Have your teacher or writing partner help you write your ideas down. Choose one and begin writing. Your teacher or partner can help you with the writing. When you are finished, check for any mistakes. Write your final copy on the following page. Draw a picture below to go with your narrative.

**1. Divide the words into syllables.**

rerun _____   redo _____

unlike _____   dislike _____

jumping _____   peanut _____

mailbox _____

retelling _____

playground _____

**2. Read each word. Find the synonym for each word in the list. Write the synonym on the line.**

big _____

present _____

shut _____

fast _____

**Word List**

little

quick

gift

close

large

small _____

**3** Read each word. Find the antonym for each word in the list.
Write the antonym on the line.

fast _____

loose _____

old _____

over _____

**Word List**

young

under

soft

slow

tight

hard _____

**4** Read each word. Find the homonym for each word in the list.
Write the homonym on the line.

ate _____

buy _____

beet _____

weak _____

**Word List**

by

fair

week

eight

beat

fare _____

Words in the dictionary are listed in alphabetical order.

**1** **Write the words in alphabetical order.**

**Word List**

dog
cat
eagle
fox
antelope
goat

**2** **Write four sentences. Use at least four words from the list.**

1.

2.

3.

4.

**3** Use the words from the word list to complete the crossword puzzle.

dog

cat

eagle

fox

antelope

goat

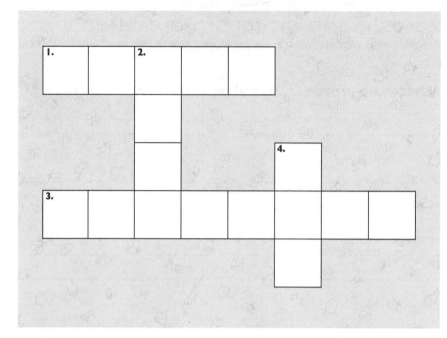

**ACROSS:**
1. This bird is our national symbol.
3. This graceful animal is a fast runner

**DOWN:**
2. This is a farm animal that eats just about anything.
4. This animal is often an orange color and lives in the forest

If the first letters of the words are the same, look at the second letters to put the words in alphabetical order.

**1** Write the words in alphabetical order, using the second letter of each word.

**Word List**

bike

bat

bob

blue

bet

button

boat

**2** Find the words from above in the word search. All the words will be going across.

| e | b | i | k | e | a | r | t | y | u | b | a | t |
| b | a | s | e | b | b | u | t | t | o | n | c | y |
| b | e | t | r | t | b | u | h | b | l | u | e | y |
| u | b | o | b | x | z | q | b | o | a | t | y | u |

**3** **Write four sentences. Use at least four of the words from the word list.**

## Word List

| bike | bat | bob | blue | bet | button | boat |
|------|-----|-----|------|-----|--------|------|

1. _____

2. _____

3. _____

4. _____

*Horizons Phonics & Reading 1, Workbook Two*

Review:
Alphabetical Order to
First & Second Letter

Name: _____

**1** Write the words in alphabetical order to the first letter.

**Word List**

Cathy

Don

Eve

Bob

Ann

Fran

_____
_____
_____
_____
_____
_____

**2** Write the words in alphabetical order to the second letter.

_____
_____
_____
_____
_____
_____

**Word List**

desk

drive

dig

door

duck

damp

**3** Read each sentence. Use the words from the word list to complete each sentence. Write the word on the line.

## Word List

| desk | drive | dig | door | duck | damp |
|------|-------|-----|------|------|------|

1. The dog likes to _____ holes.

2. She sits at her _____ in the classroom.

3. We fed the _____ some bread.

4. The ground was still _____ after the rain.

5. Please close the _____ when you leave.

**4** Read the story. Use the words from above to complete the story.

We have a pet dog who likes to _____ holes in

our yard. It is very easy for him to do when the ground is

_____ after a rain. He goes out the _____

and starts in. Dad says that he will _____ the dog

in the car and take him to dog training class. Maybe that will

stop him!

Lesson
114

Checkup:
Synonyms, Antonyms,
Homonyms

Name:

## Definition Review:

**Synonyms** are words that mean the same or almost the same thing but are spelled differently.
**Antonyms** are words that are the opposite or almost the opposite in meaning.
**Homonyms** are words that sound the same but have different spellings and different meanings.

**Read each word. Write its synonym on the line.**

glad _____

woods _____

unhappy _____

big _____

pretty _____

### Word List

forest

sad

large

beautiful

happy

silent

**2** **Read each word. Write its *antonym* on the line.**

fast _____

hard _____

full _____

big _____

cool _____

fat _____

thin

warm

soft

slow

small

empty

**3** **Read each word. Write its *homonym* on the line.**

hour _____

one _____

week _____

made _____

blue _____

buy _____

by

weak

maid

our

won

blew

## Rule Review:

When c is followed by e, i, or y, the c makes the soft sound, as in the word city.
When c is followed by a, u, o, or a consonant, the c makes the hard sound, as in the word cat.

 **Draw lines to match the pictures with the words.**

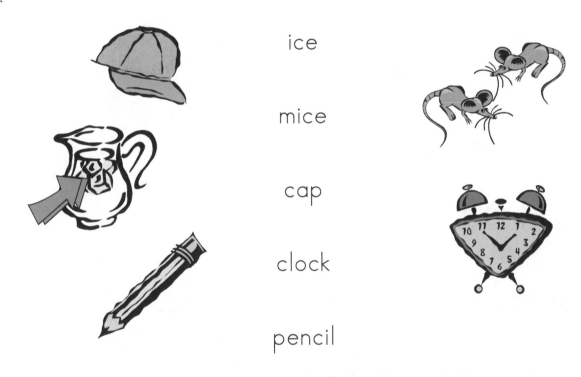

ice

mice

cap

clock

pencil

**2** **Read the words in the list. Put the words into the correct categories.**

| Hard c | Word List | Soft c |
|---|---|---|
| | cup | |
| | celery | |
| | fence | |
| | cape | |
| | rice | |
| | come | |

**3** Read each sentence. Use the words from the word list to complete each sentence. Write the word on the line.

## Word List

| cup | celery | fence | cry | rice | came |
|-----|--------|-------|-----|------|------|

1. I helped my dad paint the _____ .

2. We had chicken and _____ for supper last night.

3. Grandma and Grandpa _____ to supper.

4. I liked the way the _____ crunched when I ate it.

5. Mom and Grandma drank a _____ of tea.

6. I'm glad my baby brother did not _____ while we ate our meal.

Lesson
**116**

Checkup:
Hard & Soft g

Name:

## Rule Review:

When g is followed by e, i, or y, the g makes the soft sound, as in the word *giraffe*.
When g is followed by a, u, o, or a *consonant*, the g makes the hard sound, as in the word *gum*.

**1.** Draw lines to match the pictures with the words.

giraffe

page

gum

goat

giant

**2.** Read the words in the list. Put the words into the correct categories.

| Hard g | Word List | Soft g |
|---|---|---|
| | gum | |
| | huge | |
| | good | |
| | game | |
| | cage | |
| | gentle | |

**3** **Read the list of words. Write each word under the correct beginning sound.**

## Word List

| | | | | | |
|---|---|---|---|---|---|
| gerbil | cent | giraffe | cross | got | grow |
| cake | go | count | cell | gem | certain |

### Soft g

_____

### Hard g

_____

### Soft c

_____

### Hard c

_____

**Lesson 117**

Words with qu

Name: _____

## Rule:

The letters *qu* make the *kw* sound that you hear in *queen* and *quick*.

**1.** **Draw lines to match the pictures with the words.**

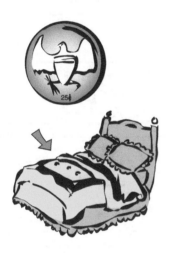

question mark

queen

quilt

quarter

**2.** **Read each sentence. Underline the word that completes each sentence. Write the word on the line.**

1. The room was _____.

    quit        quiet

2. The boy ran _____ home.

3. A _____ is worth twenty-five cents.

4. He asked his teacher a _____.

    queen        question

5. Elizabeth is the _____ of England.

    quit        queen

*Horizons Phonics & Reading 1, Workbook Two*

89

**3** Write three sentences. Use at least four of the *qu* words from this lesson.

## Word List

| question | queen | quite | quarters | quit | quiet | quickly |
|---|---|---|---|---|---|---|

1. _____

2. _____

3. _____

**4** Read the story. Use the words from the word list above to complete the story.

Tom heard the ice cream truck coming. He ran to meet

it. He knew that he needed three _____ to get

a treat. When Tom got to the truck he _____

running. The woman in the truck had _____

a lot of different things to choose

from. Tom bought his treat _____

and ran home _____ .

**Lesson**

**118**

Checkup:
Consonant Digraphs
ph & gh

Name:

## Rule:

**The consonant digraphs** *ph* **and** *gh* **can have the** *f* **sound, as in** *graph* **and** *laugh*.

**1.** **Read each word.  Put the words into the correct categories.**

### Word List

| laugh<br>fail | find<br>phone | photo<br>graph | rough<br>finish | cough |
|---|---|---|---|---|

| **f** | **ph** | **gh** |
|---|---|---|
| | | |
| | | |
| | | |
| | | |
| | | |
| | | |
| | | |

**2.** **Read the poem.  Underline all of the words that have the** *f* **sound. Remember, the** *f* **sound may be** *ph* **or** *gh*.

### The Photographs

Please don't laugh

At my photographs.

My finger got in front of the lens!

For me, it's tough

To take a photo that's not rough.

My mom says that I've done enough!

**3** Draw lines to match the pictures with the words.

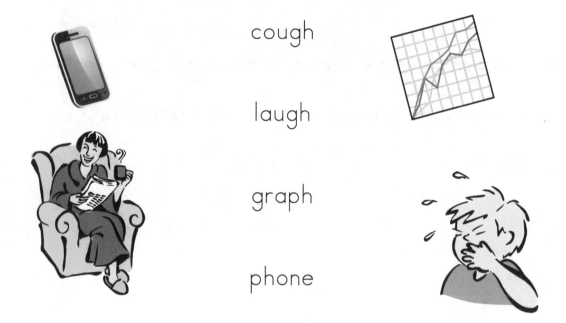

cough

laugh

graph

phone

**4** Read each sentence. Use the words from the list to complete each sentence. Write the word on the line.

## Word List

| phone | enough | nephew | rough |
|-------|--------|--------|-------|

1. The wood felt _____ because it hadn't been sanded.

2. I use a _____ to call my friend.

3. There was _____ milk for my cereal.

4. My sister's son is my _____.

**Lesson 119**

Words with
the s Sound

Name: _____

## Rule:

The letter s can stand for the s, z or sh sounds.

**1** Read each word. Put the words into the correct categories.

## Word List

| Sam | noise | close | surely | reassure |
|-----|-------|-------|--------|----------|
| raise | stay | stem | assure | |

| s as in same | s as in rise | s as in sure |
|--------------|--------------|--------------|
| | | |

**2** Read the sentences. Use some of the words from above to complete each sentence. Write the word on the line.

1. Please _____ the door when you go.

2. We _____ inside when it rains.

3. The _____ of a rose sometimes has thorns.

4. Every morning we _____ the flag.

*Horizons Phonics & Reading 1, Workbook Two*

93

**3** Read each word. Look for a word from the list with the same *s* sound. Write it next to the word with the same *s* sound.

sick _____

rose _____

sure _____

| sugar |
| noise |
| say |

**4** Use the words from the list to complete the crossword puzzle.

| raise | rose | noise | sweep | sugar |

**ACROSS:**

1. A beautiful flower that can be many different colors.

3. To lift something up.

**DOWN:**

2. A sweet powder that you can put in food or drinks.

4. Do this with a broom.

**5.** Add *s* to each of these words, then read the words to your teacher.

rai___e    noi___e    fu___e    ri___e

plea___e    tea___e    no___e    ro___e

Circle the sound the *s* makes in the words above:    s    z    sh

**6.** Add *s* to each of these words, then read the words to your teacher.

___eam    ___ame    ___ign    ___ick

Circle the sound the *s* makes in the words above:    s    z    sh

**7.** Add *s* to each of these words, then read the words to your teacher.

___ure    ___ugar    a___    sure

Circle the sound the *s* makes in the words above:    s    z    sh

**8** **Write three sentences using words with a different s sound in each sentence.**

1.

2.

3.

**Lesson**
**120**

Review:
Words with the Sounds
of f & s

Name: _____

## Rule Review:

The consonant digraphs *ph* and *gh* can stand for the *f* sound. The letter *s* can stand for the *s*, *z*, or *sh* sounds.

✏️ **Read each word. Put the words into the correct categories.**

### Word List

| fun | laugh | fan | fly | |
|-----|-------|-----|-----|--------|
| phone | nephew | phase | rough | enough |

| f | ph | gh |
|---|----|----|
| | | |
| | | |
| | | |
| | | |
| | | |
| | | |

**2** Read each word. Put the words into the correct categories.

## Word List

| Sam | noise | sing | raise | |
|---|---|---|---|---|
| please | sugar | stay | surely | assure |

| s = sun | s = sure | s = rise |
|---|---|---|
| _____ | _____ | _____ |
| _____ | _____ | _____ |
| _____ | _____ | _____ |
| _____ | _____ | _____ |
| _____ | _____ | _____ |
| _____ | _____ | _____ |

**3** Read each sentence. Underline the word that completes each sentence. Write the word on the line.

1. Jason is my _____ .

   star     cousin

2. I am _____ that I know the answer.

   sure     same

3. Dad puts _____ in his tea.

   sweet     sugar

4. The day _____ flew by!

   surely     some

5. It is my job to _____ the flag every day.

   rode     raise

**1** Put the names in alphabetical order to the first letter.

Mark
Janet
Ann
Brad
Luke
Carol
Dan
Eve

1. _____          5. _____

2. _____          6. _____

3. _____          7. _____

4. _____          8. _____

**2** Put the words in alphabetical order to the second letter.

1. _____          4. _____

2. _____          5. _____

3. _____          6. _____

cream
city
cake
climb
cent
come

**3** Read each word. Put the words into the correct categories

| seal | noise | sum | sure | sugar | rose |

| S = sh sound | S = s sound | S = z sound |
| --- | --- | --- |
| | | |
| | | |

**4** Circle the sentence that tells what it is in the picture.

The **q**ueen has
a crown.

The king has
a red hat.

She is making cookies.
She is making a **q**uilt.

This is a **q**uill pen.
You must be **q**uick.

**5** Use the words from the list to answer the riddles.

| phone | rough | laugh | cough | enough |
|-------|-------|-------|-------|--------|

1. This is what you might do
   if you have a cold.

2. This is the way that wood
   feels before you sand it.

3. When you are full, you
   have had _____ .

4. You use this when you
   want to call someone.

5. When something is funny,
   you do this.

 **Write a story about an imaginary animal.**

In this lesson you will be writing an imaginative story. This is a story that you make up yourself. It doesn't have to be true. Your story can be funny, silly, serious, anything that you want it to be.

This story will be about an imaginary animal. Make up an animal and think about it. When would it have lived, or would it be alive now? What does the animal do? Where does it live? Does it live on its own, or is it a pet? You might make your animal have some kind of an adventure, or perform a good deed.

Have your teacher or writing partner help you think of ideas. Write them down. After you write your ideas down, you can start your story. Write your story on a piece of paper first, then write the final copy on the next page. Have your teacher or writing partner help you check for spelling or punctuation mistakes before you write your final copy.

## Rule:

Sometimes y can make the long ē or ī sound.  The y is usually at the end of the word when it makes the long ē or ī sound.

 **Draw lines to match the pictures with the words.**

baby

cry

city

penny

fly

puppy

**2** **Write three sentences.  Use all six of the words from above.**

1.

2.

3.

**3** Read each sentence. Use the words from the list to complete each sentence. Write the word on the line

## Word List

| cry | penny | city | baby | fly |
|-----|-------|------|------|-----|

1. We live in the _____ .

2. I have a _____ sister.

3. A _____ is worth one cent.

4. A bird can _____ .

5. The loud noise made the baby _____ .

**4** Use the words from the list to complete the crossword puzzle.

nearby

funny

fly

try

**ACROSS:**

1. You must always _____ to do your best.

2. Jokes are meant to be _____ .

**DOWN:**

2. I like watching the birds _____ .

3. My friend lives _____ .

## Definition:

A *contraction* is a word that is made from two words. Two words are put together, and one or more letters are left out. In contractions formed with the word *will*, an apostrophe (') is used in place of the letters that are left out.

**Examples:** *they will = they'll, you will = you'll* and *I will = I'll*.

**1** Write the contraction for each set of two words.

they will _____        we will _____

I will _____        you will _____

she will _____        it will _____

he will _____

**2** Read each contraction. Find the two words that go with it.
Write the words on the lines.

I'll _____ _____        they'll _____ _____

she'll _____ _____        you'll _____ _____

we'll _____ _____        it'll _____ _____

he'll _____ _____

**3** Read each contraction. Think about the letter or letters that were left out when the contraction was made. Write the missing letters on the line.

you'll  _____        I'll  _____

he'll  _____        it'll  _____

she'll  _____

**4** Write four sentences. Use at least four contractions from this lesson.

1. _____

_____

2. _____

_____

3. _____

_____

4. _____

_____

Lesson
**124**

Checkup:
Contractions with Not

Name: _____

## Definition:

A *contraction* is a word that is made from two words. Two words are put together, and one or more letters are left out. In contractions formed with the word *not*, an apostrophe (') is used in place of the letters that are left out. Examples: *cannot = can't*, *do not = don't*.

**1.** **Read each contraction. Write the two words that make up each contraction. Write the words on the lines.**

don't _____ _____

won't _____ _____

can't _____ _____

shouldn't _____ _____

didn't _____ _____

couldn't _____ _____

wouldn't _____ _____

**2.** **Write the letter or letters that were left out of the contraction.**

don't _____ shouldn't _____

wouldn't _____ can't _____

won't _____

*Horizons Phonics & Reading 1, Workbook Two*

107

**3** Draw lines to match the contractions with the two words that go with it.

wouldn't

couldn't

didn't

can't

won't

shouldn't

don't

do not

cannot

could not

should not

will not

would not

did not

**4** Write four sentences. Use at least four of the contractions from this lesson.

1. _____

2. _____

3. _____

4. _____

 **Write a short poem about your favorite food.**

In this lesson you will write a short poem. Poems can rhyme, or not. You will write a poem about your favorite food. Think about this food and why it is your favorite. What do you like about it? Start with those ideas. Try to include in your poem some of the contractions that you have learned about. You might want to look at some poetry books before you start.

Your poem should be at least three lines long. Have your teacher or writing partner help you write your poem. He or she can help you with spelling and ideas. Write your first copy on a piece of paper. Write your final copy on the following page and draw a picture to go with your poem.

**Lesson 126**

Checkup:
Contractions with Have

Name: _____

## Definition:

A *contraction* is a word that is made from two words.  Two words are put together, and one or more letters are left out.  In contractions formed with the word *have*, an apostrophe (') is used in place of the letters that are left out.

**Examples:** *I have* = *I've*, *you have* = *you've*.

**1.** Read each contraction.  Write the two words that make up each contraction.

I've _____ _____

we've _____ _____

they've _____ _____

you've _____ _____

**2.** Draw lines to match each contraction with the two words that go with it.

you've                     we have

we've                      I have

they've                    you have

I've                        they have

*Horizons Phonics & Reading 1, Workbook Two*

111

**3** What letter or letters have been left out of each contraction? Write the letter or letters on the line.

I've _____

you've _____

they've _____

we've _____

**4** Write three sentences. Use at least three of the contractions from this lesson.

**Word List**

I've      we've      they've      you've

1. _____

_____

2. _____

_____

3. _____

_____

## Definition:

A *contraction* is a word that is made from two words. Two words are put together, and one or more letters are left out. In contractions formed with the word *is*, an apostrophe (') is used in place of the letters that are left out. Examples: *he is* = *he's*, *she is* = *she's*.

**1.** Read each contraction. Write the two words that make up each contraction. Write the words on the lines.

he's _____ _____          it's _____ _____

she's _____ _____

**2.** Read each contraction. Match each contraction with the words. Write the letter on the line.

she's _____

it's _____

he's _____

a. it is

b. she is

c. he is

**3.** Read each contraction.
What letters were left out? Write the letter or letters on the line.

it's _____          she's _____          he's _____

**Write three sentences.**
**Use one of the contractions from this lesson in each sentence.**

## Word List

| he's | she's | it's |
|------|-------|------|

1. _____

2. _____

3. _____

Lesson
128

Checkup:
Contractions with
Am & Us

Name:

## Definition:

A *contraction* is a word that is made from two words. Two words are put together, and one or more letters are left out. In contractions formed with the words *am* and *us*, an apostrophe (') is used in place of the letters that are left out. Examples: *I am* = *I'm*, *let us* = *let's*.

**1** Write the two words that make up each contraction.

I'm                                                           let's

_____                              _____

_____                              _____

**2** Draw lines to match the picture with the phrase that describes it.

Let's hike to the
top of the hill.

Let's play outside.

I'm very sleepy.

I'm going inside.

**3** Read each contraction.
What letters are left out?
Write the letter or letters that were left out on the line.

I'm _____     let's _____

**4** Write a sentence for each contraction.

1. _____

_____

2. _____

_____

**Checkup:**
**Contractions with Are**

Name:

## Definition:

A *contraction* is a word that is made from two words. Two words are put together, and one or more letters are left out. In contractions formed with the word *are*, an apostrophe (') is used in place of the letters that are left out. Examples: *you are = you're*, *they are = they're*.

**1.** Read each contraction.
Write the two words that make up each contraction.
Write the words on the lines.

they're _____  _____

we're _____  _____

you're _____  _____

**2.** Draw lines to match the contraction with the two words that go with it.

we're

you're

they're

you are

they are

we are

**3.** Read each contraction.
What letters are left out?
Write the letter or letters that were left out on the line.

you're _____     they're _____     we're _____

**Write a sentence for each contraction.**

| you're | they're | we're |
|--------|---------|-------|

1. _____

2. _____

3. _____

## Lesson 130

Checkup:
R-Controlled Vowel ar

Name: _____

### Rule:

An **r** after a vowel makes the vowel sound different from a short or long sound.
Examples: *hard*, *part*, *car*.

**1** Use the words from the list to label the pictures.

bark
star
car
jar
farm

**2** Read each sentence. Use the words from the list to complete each sentence. Write the word on the line.

### Word List

| start | farm | part | lark | tar | mark |
|-------|------|------|------|-----|------|

1. I saw only _____ of the play.

2. That bird is a _____.

3. Mom couldn't _____ the car.

4. The workers used _____ to fix the hole in the street.

5. I made a _____ with my pen.

6. My friend lives on a _____.

**3** Read each sentence. Use the words from the list to complete each sentence. Write the word on the line.

## Word List

| hard | car | park | dark | start |
|------|-----|------|------|-------|

1. Mark and Bart went to the _____ .

2. Mark's mom took them in her _____ .

3. She told them they could stay until _____ .

4. They played _____ while they were at the park.

5. Then they got in the car to _____ for home.

**4** Add *ar* to each of the words below, then read the words to your teacher.

_____ ch    ch_____ m    d_____ t

c_____ t    sh_____ k    m_____ sh

sc_____    y_____ d    st_____ ch

sm_____ t    sh_____ p    sp_____ k

**What do you remember?**

**Test 13**
Lessons 121–130
27 points

Name: _____

**1.** Read each sentence. Use a word from the list to complete each sentence. Write the word on the line.

**Word List**

| why | pretty | city | by |

1. Jack lives in the _____ .

2. The lights are _____ .

3. The bird flew _____ .

4. I don't know _____ that happened.

**2.** Draw lines to match the pictures with the words.

park

shark

car

bark

jar

**3** **Write the two words that make up each contraction.**

shouldn't _____ _____

haven't _____ _____

aren't _____ _____     won't _____ _____

didn't _____ _____     I'll _____ _____

she'll _____ _____     we'll _____ _____

you've _____ _____     we've _____ _____

I've _____ _____     let's _____ _____

he's _____ _____     she's _____ _____

I'm _____ _____     you're _____ _____

we're _____ _____     they're _____ _____

## Rule:

An *r* after a vowel makes the vowel sound different from a short or long sound.
**Examples:** *corn*, *for*, *born*.

**1** Use the words from the list to answer the riddles.

### Word List

| storm | popcorn | thorn | horn | fork |
|-------|---------|-------|------|------|

1. You can pop and eat this.

2. This makes noise.

3. This has rain, wind, and thunder.

4. You eat with this.

5. This is a sharp point on a rose stem.

**2** Add *or* to each of the words below, then read the words to your teacher.

p _____    ch    ch _____    e    sc _____    n

f _____    k    n _____    th    th _____    n

t _____    ch    w _____    n    t _____    n

st _____    k    sh _____    t    sc _____    ch

**3** Use the words from the list to complete the crossword puzzle.

porch

born

horn

north

**ACROSS:**

1. A baby comes in to the world by being _____ .

2. This is a direction: _____ , south, east, and west.

**DOWN:**

3. The lady honked her _____ .

4. Some houses have one of these on the front.

**4** Look at each picture. Circle the word that names the picture.

cork   fork      horn   born      corn   thorn      more   shore      tore   store

**5** Read each sentence. Use the words from above to complete each sentence. Write the words on the lines.

1. We use a _____ to eat our food.

2. The boy _____ the paper.

3. We went down to the _____ to look for crabs.

4. I want to have some _____ play time.

*Horizons Phonics & Reading 1, Workbook Two*

Lesson
**132**

Review:
R-Controlled Vowels
ar & or

Name: _____

## Rule:

An **r** after a vowel makes the vowel sound different from a short or long sound.
**Examples:** *corn, form, born, are, far, barn.*

**1** Read the words. Put each word in the correct category.

| ar | Word List | or |
|----|-----------|----|
| _____ | barn | _____ |
| _____ | start | _____ |
| _____ | form | _____ |
| _____ | farm | _____ |
| _____ | born | _____ |
| _____ | forty | _____ |

**2** Use the words from the list to answer the riddles.

1. _____ comes after thirty-nine.

2. Not close, but _____.

3. Not finish, but _____.

4. A cow lives on a _____.

5. It's black and sticky and is used to fix
holes in roads. _____

**Word List**

farm

far

tar

forty

start

**3** Draw lines to match the pictures with the words.

horn

porch

farm

star

horse

**4** Read the story. Use the words from above to complete the story.

Kay's grandma and grandpa live on a _____.

They have a _____ named Betsy. Kay likes to ride

Betsy. She also likes to sit on the front _____ of

the house. The last time Kay was there, she saw a falling

_____. She made a wish.

## Rule:

An *r* after a vowel makes the vowel sound different from a short or long sound.
Examples: *her*, *clerk*, *letter*.

**1.** Look at the pictures. Use the words from the list to write the name for each picture.

### Word List

| farmer | clerk | fern |
|---|---|---|

_____   _____   _____

**2.** Read each sentence. Underline the word that completes each sentence. Write the word on the line.

1. She didn't _____ want to go there again.
   ever        more

2. Mark wrote a _____ to his friend.
   summer       letter

3. She knows many Bible _____.
   visit        verses

4. John went _____ the bridge.
   under        were

5. We _____ having fun.
   what         were

**3** Write three sentences. Use at least three of the words from the list.

## Word List

| farmer | clerk | fern | river | hammer |
| --- | --- | --- | --- | --- |

1. _____

2. _____

3. _____

**4** Add *er* to each of the words below, then read the words to your teacher.

st_____      n bett_____      nev_____

cl_____      k p_____      ch t_____      m

h_____      d lett_____      f_____      n

wint_____      summ_____      und_____

## Rule:

An **r** after a vowel makes the vowel sound different from a short or long sound.
**Examples:** *first*, *skirt*, *dirt*.

**1** Draw lines to match the pictures with the words.

skirt

dirty

bird

girl

shirt

**2** Read each sentence. Use the words from the list to complete each sentence.
Write the word on the line.

### Word List

| shirt | first | girl | dirt | skirt | bird |
| --- | --- | --- | --- | --- | --- |

1. The _____ is wearing a _____ .

2. Joe has a pet _____ .

3. Don is _____ in line.

4. Dan is wearing a blue _____ .

5. The dog likes to dig in the _____ .

**3** Use the words from the list to answer the riddles.

1. Not second, but _____.

2. Not a boy, but a _____.

3. Not clean, but full of _____.

4. Not pants, but a _____.

**4** Add *ir* to each of the words below, then read the words to your teacher.

f _____  m sw _____  l th _____  st

f _____  st d _____  ty sm _____  k

wh _____  l ch _____  p sh _____  t

st _____  b _____  th tw _____  l

**Lesson**
**135**

Review:
R-Controlled Vowels
er & ir

Name:

## Rule:

An **r** after a vowel makes the vowel sound different from a short or long sound.
**Examples:** *her, clerk, letter, first, dirt, skirt.*

**1** Read each word. Put the words into the correct categories.

| er | Word List | ir |
|----|-----------|-----|
|    | third     |    |
|    | her       |    |
|    | first     |    |
|    | clerk     |    |
|    | dirt      |    |
|    | ever      |    |

**2** Read each sentence. Use the words from above to complete each sentence. Write the word on the line.

1. Irma is _____ best friend.

2. The dog rolled in the _____ .

3. The store _____ was nice.

4. Have you _____ been to Irma's house?

5. Laura is in first grade, and her brother is in _____ grade.

**3** Use the words from the list to complete the crossword puzzle.

skirt     third     dirt     river     bird

**ACROSS:**

3. The _____ flew in the sky.

5. After second comes _____ .

**DOWN:**

1. My mom got a new _____ .

2. The boat floated down the _____ .

4. The farmer filled the hole with _____ .

**4** Look at each picture.
Find the word that goes with it. Write the letter for the word on the line.

_____

a. dirt

b. girl

c. skirt

d. bird

e. shirt

## Rule:

**An r after a vowel makes the vowel sound different from a short or long sound.**
**Examples:** *nurse*, *fur*, *burn*.

**1.** Draw lines to match the pictures with the words.

turtle

burn

nurse

fur

purse

**2.** Read each sentence. Use the words from above to complete each sentence. Write the word on the line

1. The _____ went into its shell.

2. Jim got a _____ when he touched the hot stove.

3. The _____ at the doctor's office takes care of us.

4. Mom carries a big brown _____ to keep her things in.

5. Our dog has black _____ to keep him warm.

**3**  **Read the story.  Use the words from the list to complete the story.**

### Word List

| curl | turn | turtle |
|------|------|--------|

Carol is happy because her birthday is coming soon.
_____

Carol will _____ seven. She will have a party and
_____

invite her friends and family. She plans to _____

her hair so that she will look pretty. Even her pet
_____

_____ will be there!

**4**  **Add _ur_ to each of the words below, then read the words to your teacher.**

b _____ st     c _____ l     ch _____ ch

h _____ t     pl _____ al     c _____ b

t _____ n     t _____ tle     l _____ ch

ch _____ n     sp _____     bl _____

## Lesson 137

**Writing Lesson:**
**Journal Entry**

Name:

**Write a pretend journal entry.**

A journal is a place where you write down special things that happen to you. You can also use a journal to write down your feelings or anything else that you would like to write about. A journal is your special book to keep about yourself.

For this lesson, pretend that you spent a day visiting a farm. Write about the things that you did. What did the farm look like? What animals were there? What did you do there? Would you like to live on a farm?

Have your teacher or writing partner help you write down your ideas on paper, then you can begin your journal entry. Remember, you are telling this story about yourself. After you get help correcting any mistakes, write your final copy on the following page.

## Rule:

The prefix *re-* usually means *to do again*.
Examples: *reread* = to read again; *repack* = to pack again.

**1.** Read each word. Read the meanings. Match the words with their meanings. Write the letter of the correct answer on the line.

reread _____

retie _____

rewrite _____

rewind _____

a. to do again
b. to pack again
c. to load again
d. to read again
e. to write again
f. to make again
g. to tie again
h. to wind again

_____ redo

_____ repack

_____ reload

_____ remake

**2.** Draw lines to match the pictures with the words.

remake

reread

repack

retie

rewrite

**3** **Read each word. Write the base word for each one.**

reread _____     remake _____

retie _____      reuse _____

rewrite _____     rewind _____

**4** **Write four sentences. Use at least eight of the words from the word list.**

## Word List

| reread | rewrite | redo | reload | |
|--------|---------|------|--------|------|
| retie | rewind | repack | remake | reuse |

1. _____

2. _____

3. _____

4. _____

**Lesson 139**

Checkup:
Prefix un-

Name: _____

## Rule:

The prefix *un-* usually means the *opposite* of the original word.
Examples: <u>un</u>button, <u>un</u>lock.

**1.** Look at each picture.  Use the words from the list to write the word that goes with each picture.

| unhappy |
| unbutton |
| unload |
| unwrap |

_____

_____

_____

_____

**2.** Read each sentence.  Use the words from above to complete each sentence.

1. The boy was _____ about losing his toy.

2. She can _____ her coat by herself.

3. On your birthday, you _____ your gifts.

4. The men will _____ the moving van.

*Horizons Phonics & Reading 1, Workbook Two*

139

## 3  Write the base words.

unload _____     untie _____

unbuckle _____     unhappy _____

undo _____     unsafe _____

## 4  Write four sentences.  Use at least six words from the lesson.

### Word List

| unhappy | unpack | unload | undo | |
|---------|--------|--------|------|---------|
| unbutton | unwrap | unbuckle | untie | unsafe |

1. _____

2. _____

3. _____

4. _____

## Rule:

The prefix *dis-* means the *opposite* of the original word.  Examples: *disobey*, *displeased*.

**1** **Write the base words.**

disagree _____     disgrace _____

disorder _____     discover _____

disobey _____      displease _____

dislike _____      distrust _____

**2** **Read each word.  Read the meanings.  Match each word with its meaning. Write the letter on the line.**

disobey _____

dislike _____

disagree _____

disorder _____

distrust _____

a. to not obey

b. not in order

c. to not trust

d. to not like

e. to not agree

**3** **Write five sentences.  Use at least *five* words from this lesson.**

### Word List

| disagree | disobey | discover | displease |
|----------|---------|----------|-----------|
| disorder | disgrace | dislike | distrust |

1. _____

2. _____

3. _____

4. _____

5. _____

# What do you know?

## Test 14
### Lessons 131–140
### 24 points

Name: _____

✏ **Read each sentence. Use the words from the list to complete each sentence.**

## Word List

| third | turn | her | burn | |
|-------|------|-----|------|------|
| shirt | far | born | flower | were |

1. Grandma's house is _____ away from our house.

2. John is _____ in line.

3. _____ name is Joan.

4. _____ you at school today?

5. Jack is wearing a blue _____ .

6. The car made a wrong _____ .

7. Mark got a bad _____ when he touched the hot stove.

8. John's baby brother was just _____ today.

9. A rose is a pretty _____ .

**2** **Draw lines to match the words with their meanings.**

redo                    to read again

untie                    opposite of tie

disobey                    to do again

unlock                    opposite of do

reread                    to not obey

distrust                    to not trust

undo                    opposite of lock

**3** **Look at the pictures. Circle the correct r-controlled vowel.**

ar er ir or ur

ar er ir or ur

ar er ir or ur

ar er ir or ur

ar er ir or ur

ar er ir or ur

ar er ir or ur

ar er ir or ur

**Lesson**
**141**

Checkup:
Capitalization &
Punctuation

Name: _____
_____

**1** Rewrite these sentences, adding the correct punctuation and capitalization.

are jim and jan ready yet

_____

_____

mrs davis is my moms friend

_____

_____

**2** Read the sentences.  Draw a circle around each punctuation mark.  Underline
the exact words that are being said by both people.

"Let's go to the park," said Grandma. "I can watch you

run and jump and play on the swings and the slide."

"Oh boy!" shouted Erik. "May we stop and pick up my

friend John?"

"Sure," replied Grandma. "Are you ready to go now?"

"Yes," said Erik. "John's house is right on our way to the

park. Thank you, Grandma!"

How would you like to go sledding asked Dad

Great we yelled

Climb in the car said Dad

We found a great hill for sledding  It was steep and long

May we please do this again next week we asked Dad

## Rule:

When x comes at the end of a word, it is usually pronounced *ks*. Examples: *box*, *fox*.
When x comes at the beginning of a word, it usually has the *z* sound. Example: *xylophone*.

**1** Match the pictures with the words.

ax

box

ox

fox

**2** Read each sentence. Underline the word that completes each sentence.
Write the word on the line.

1. The _____ ran after the rabbit.
   fox    sax

2. The toys are kept in a _____.
   fox    box

3. The _____ stood in the field, chewing some grass.
   ax    ox

4. Dad chopped the wood with an _____.
   ox    ax

5. Mom will _____ the broken chair.
   six    fix

## 3  Read the story.  Use the words from the list to complete the story.

| Word List | | | |
|---|---|---|---|
| fox | relax | fix | box |

Mary wanted to come home and just _____ .

When she got home, she saw that she needed to _____

the broken vase. She also saw a _____ of things to put

away. Things were a mess. It looked like a _____ had

run through her house.

## 4  Add x to each of the words below, then read the words to your teacher.

mi _____      fi _____      fo _____

Ma _____      ta _____      te _____ t

wa _____      si _____      bo _____

rela _____      ylophone _____

## Lesson
## 143

**Checkup:**
**Alphabetical Order**
**to the First Letter**

**Name:** _____

**Put the words in alphabetical order.**

dog

mouse

cat

snake

boar

rabbit

eagle

ferret

goat

anteater

**2** Write three sentences using at least three of the animal words listed below.

| Word List | | | | |
|---|---|---|---|---|
| dog | cat | boar | eagle | goat |
| mouse | snake | rabbit | ferret | anteater |

1. _____

2. _____

3. _____

**3** Read the story.  Use the animal names from above to complete the story.

Joshua's _____ barked all day. He was barking

at the black _____ that lived across the street.

Joshua's neighbors weren't happy. They would have liked it

if he owned a quiet pet, like a slithery _____ or

a fluffy white _____ with long ears.

Checkup:
Alphabetical Order to
the Second Letter

Name: _____

 **Put the names in alphabetical order.**

| | | | | |
|---|---|---|---|---|
| Sam | Sidney | Sue | Sharon | Seth | Stanley | Scott |

 **Use the words from the list to answer the riddles.**

## Word List

eagle        goat        dog        snake        rabbit

1. This is an animal that barks.

2. This bird is our national symbol.

3. This animal has horns and will eat
   just about anything.

4. This animal has soft fur and long ears.

5. This animal is a reptile and slithers.

**3** Write three sentences. Use four of the names from the word list.

## Word List

Sam    Sidney    Sue    Sharon    Sean    Stanley    Scott

1. 

2. 

3. 

**4** Draw a picture about one of your sentences.

Lesson

145

Review:
Plural Words Ending
in ss or s

Name: _____

## Rule:

When a word ends in **ss** or **s**, you usually add **es** at the end to make the word plural.

**1** Look at the pictures.  Circle the pictures that show more than one.

**2** Read each word.  Rewrite each word with its plural ending.

dress _____

class _____

pass _____

cross _____

glass _____

**Use the words from the list to complete the crossword puzzle.**

classes     grasses     passes     glasses     dresses

**ACROSS:**

1. I am taking three _____ this year.

3. Mom wears _____ so that she can see better.

**DOWN:**

2. Jan has two special _____ that she likes to wear.

3. We planted two kinds of _____ in our yard.

## Rule Review:

**When a word ends in x, you usually add es at the end to make the word plural.**

**1** **Read each word.  Write the plural form of each word on the line.**

fox _____        fix _____

box _____        tax _____

ax _____

**2** **Use the plural words from above to complete each sentence.**
**Write the word on the line.**

1. The dogs chased the two _____ through the woods.

2. Dad made two _____ to my bike.

3. He sharpened the _____ for cutting the wood.

4. We packed our things in _____ .

**3** **Use the words from the list to answer the riddles.**

## Word List

| foxes | axes | prefixes | boxes | suffixes |

_____

1. These come at the beginning of words.  _____

2. These wild animals live in the forest.  _____

3. These come at the end of words.  _____

4. These are used to chop wood.  _____

5. You pack things in these.  _____

Review:
Plural Words Ending in sh

Name: _____

## Rule:

When a word ends in *sh*, you usually add *es* at the end to make the word plural.

**1.** **Read each word.  Write the plural form of each word on the line.**

brush  _____        wish  _____

dish  _____        crash  _____

flash  _____        dash  _____

ash  _____        gash  _____

**2.** **Read each sentence.**
**Use the correct plural words from above to complete the sentences.**

1. There are many_____ in the kitchen cupboard.

2. I like to make birthday _____ when I blow out
   the candles.

3. We saw three car _____ on the freeway.

**3**  Look at the pictures. Circle the pictures that show more than one.

**4**  Write the base words.

brushes  _____

crashes  _____

dishes  _____

wishes  _____

## Rule Review:

When a word ends in **ch**, you usually add **es** at the end to make the word plural.

**1.** Read each word. Write the plural form of each word on the line.

peach _____

watch _____

patch _____

lunch _____

church _____

coach _____

**2.** Look at each picture. Circle the pictures that show more than one.

**3** Read each sentence. Use the plural words from the word list to complete each sentence. Write the word on the line.

| Word List | | | | | |
| --- | --- | --- | --- | --- | --- |
| peaches | watches | patches | bunches | churches | touches |

1. We bought fresh _____ at the store.

2. There are six different _____ in our town.

3. Mom sewed _____ on my jeans.

4. John has two different _____ to wear on his wrist.

**4** Write the base word for each plural word.

coaches _____      churches _____

peaches _____      touches _____

bunches _____      lunches _____

*Horizons Phonics & Reading 1, Workbook Two*

Lesson
149
Review:
Plural Words Ending in
a Vowel plus y

Name: _____

## Rule Review:

**If a word ends in a vowel and a y, just add s to the end of the word to make it plural.
Examples:** *boy/boys, tray/trays, day/days.*

**1.** **Read each sentence. Look at the base word. Complete the sentence
by writing the plural form of the base word on the line.**

1. Mary took two _____ of food to the table.
   tray

2. Lynn _____ with her friend after school.
   play

3. The house has two _____.
   chimney

4. They had two _____ for Thanksgiving.
   turkey

5. There are twelve _____ in the class.
   boy

**2.** **Read each word. Write the plural form of each word on the line.**

day _____          stay _____

jay _____          key _____

monkey _____       chimney _____

**3** Write three sentences.
Use at least three of the plural words from this lesson.

**Word List**

trays

plays

chimneys

turkeys

boys

days

jays

monkeys

stays

keys

1. _____

2. _____

3. _____

**4** Read the story. Complete the story using words from the list.

**Word List**

| days | monkeys | stays | turkeys | plays |
|------|---------|-------|---------|-------|

Jane always _____ with her friend Lucy

after school. She _____ there until dinnertime

on most _____. Sometimes they pretend that

they are _____ living in the jungle. Other

times they pretend that they are _____ and

gobble around the house.

## Rule:

Some words have plural forms that are irregular.  Examples: *goose/geese*, *mouse/mice*.

**1** **Draw lines to match the pictures with the words.**

geese

feet

men

mice

children

teeth

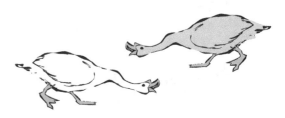

**2** **Write the plural forms of the words.**

mouse  _____

child  _____

tooth  _____

goose  _____

foot  _____

man  _____

**3** Use the words from the list to complete each sentence.

## Word List

| teeth | geese | mice | children |
|-------|-------|------|----------|

1. There were three _____ on the farm.

2. The _____ got away from the cat.

3. The _____ are playing on the playground.

4. A shark has sharp _____.

**4** Use the words from the list to complete the crossword puzzle.

| children |
|----------|
| men |
| mice |
| feet |

**ACROSS:**

1. Plural form of man.
2. Plural form of child.

**DOWN:**

1. Plural form of mouse.
3. Plural form of foot.

**1.** **Write a sentence to go with each picture.**
**Include the word under the picture in the sentence.**

1. fox

_____
_____
_____

2. box

_____
_____
_____

3. ax

_____
_____
_____

**2.** **Put the words in alphabetical order to the first letter.**

desk

chair

table

blinds

sofa

lamp

_____
_____
_____
_____
_____
_____

**3** **Put the words in alphabetical order to the second letter.**

Brenda

Beth

Bob

Barbara

Bill

_____

**4** **Read each word. Write the plural form of each word on the line.**

class _____    key _____

dress _____    grass _____

box _____    crunch _____

brush _____    mouse _____

bunch _____    goose _____

monkey _____    tooth _____

## Rule:
**Some plural forms of words are spelled the same way as the singular forms.**
**Examples:** *sheep*, *deer*, *moose*, *elk*, *fish*.

**1** **Draw lines to match the pictures with the words.**

moose

fish

elk

sheep

deer

**2** **Read each sentence. Underline the word that correctly completes each sentence. Write the word on the line.**

1. The _____ were running through the forest.
   deer      dear

2. _____ give us wool for sweaters.
   Shout      Sheep

3. There are a lot of _____ in the ocean.
   foot      fish

4. _____ live in Alaska.
   Mouse      Moose

**3** **Read the story. Use the words from the list to complete the story.**

Last summer we took a trip to Alaska. We saw lots of

huge _____ . We saw many _____

flying by. We also saw some _____ . The does

had fawns with them. There were a lot of _____

swimming in the lakes and rivers. It was a great trip!

**4** **Write three sentences. Use at least three of the plural words from this lesson.**

1. _____

_____

2. _____

_____

3. _____

_____

**Possessives**

Name: _____

## Rule:

The possessive form of a word shows that someone owns or has something. To make a singular noun show possession, add an *apostrophe* and an *s* (*'s*) at the end of the word. Examples: *Mary's* hat, *John's* ball.

**1** **Match the pictures with the phrases.**

the girl's doll

the lady's bag

the man's robe

the boy's cast

the baby's rattle

**2** **Read each sentence. Underline the word that completes each sentence. Write the word on the line.**

1. The _____ desk is near the door.
   Tom            teacher's

2. The _____ hat is on his head.
   man's            men

3. The _____ collar is brown.
   dig            dog's

4. My _____ birthday is tomorrow.
   sister's            suit

5. Can your _____ dog do tricks?
   bother            brother's

### 3 Write the possessive form of each word.

dancer _____

girl _____

mom _____

cat _____

friend _____

doctor _____

### 4 Write four sentences about places that you like to visit.
Use at least four possessive nouns, one for each sentence.

1. _____

2. _____

3. _____

4. _____

Lesson

**153**

Review:
Possessives &
Contractions

Name: _____

## Rule Review:

The possessive form of a word shows that someone owns or has something.
To make a singular noun show possession, add an *apostrophe* and an *s* (*'s*) at the
end of the word. Examples: *Mary's hat*, *John's ball*.

A *contraction* is a word that is made from two words. Two words are put together,
and one or more letters are left out. Examples: *cannot = can't*, *we will = we'll*,
*I have = I've*, *you are = you're*, *let us = let's*, *it is = it's*.

**Read each sentence. Underline the word that completes the sentence.
Write the word on the line.**

1. _____ going to the zoo.
   I'm      We've

2. _____ have a lot of fun there.
   They've      I'll

3. My _____ dad is taking us.
   friend's      he's

4. I can't wait to see the _____ new cubs.
   it's      lion's

5. _____ sure that I'll enjoy myself!
   She'll      I'm

**2** Read the story.  Circle all the words that are possessives or contractions.  Answer the questions using words from the list.

## Word List

| John's | careful | hats | sled | mittens |

It's fun to go sledding in the winter. We'll be going a lot this year. My friends John and Peter always bring their sleds. John's sled is faster than Peter's. Mom tells us that we shouldn't forget to wear our warm hats and mittens. She's also telling us to be careful!

1. What is fun to do in the winter?

2. Whose sled is the fastest?

3. What two things does Mom tell the boys to wear?

**3** Write two sentences.  Write one sentence containing a *possessive* noun and one sentence containing a *contraction*.

1.

2.

**Lesson 154**

Checkup: Suffixes

Name: _____

## Rule Review:

If a word with a short vowel sound ends in a single consonant, you usually double the consonant before adding a suffix that begins with a vowel.
**Examples:** *tag*/*tagged*, *tagging*; *big*/*bigger*, *biggest*; *fat*/*fatter*, *fattest*.

**1.** Add a suffix to the base word to make a new word. Write the new word on the line. You can add *-ed*, *-er*, or *-ing*. Be sure that the new word makes sense.

tag _____     sad _____

hot _____     fit _____

mad _____     wrap _____

big _____     set _____

nap _____

**2.** Read each sentence. Use the words from the list to complete each sentence. Write the word on the line.

1. Mark is _____ presents.

2. My cat is the _____ .

3. The baby was _____ in his crib.

4. The sun is _____ in the west.

5. It was the _____ day of the summer.

**Word List**

biggest

hottest

wrapping

napping

setting

**3** Write five sentences. Use at least five of the new words from Exercise 1.

1. _____

2. _____

3. _____

4. _____

5. _____

Writing Lesson:
Friendly Letter

Name: _____

✏ **Write a friendly letter.**

A friendly letter contains five parts:

1. Heading
2. Greeting
3. Body
4. Closing
5. Signature

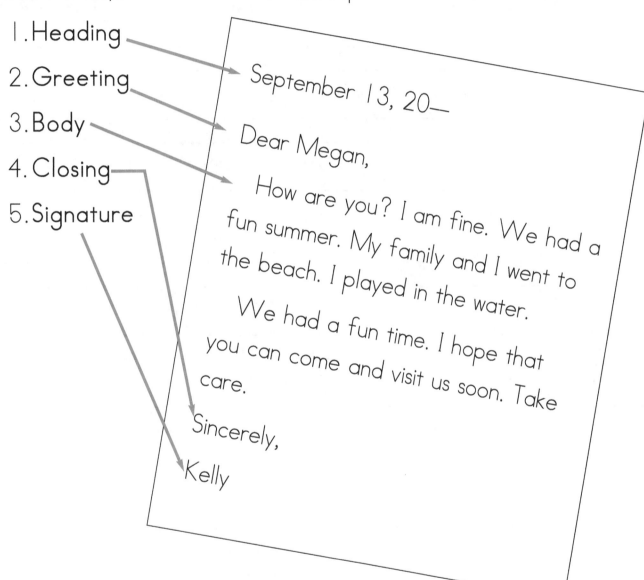

September 13, 20—

Dear Megan,

How are you? I am fine. We had a fun summer. My family and I went to the beach. I played in the water. We had a fun time. I hope that you can come and visit us soon. Take care.

Sincerely,

Kelly

You may write your letter to a friend or relative. Have your teacher or writing partner help you. He or she can also help you correct any mistakes in spelling or punctuation. Write your first copy on a piece of paper. Write your final copy on the following page.

Review:
Suffixes with Words
Ending in Silent e

Name: _____

## Rule Review:

If a word ends in *silent e*, drop the e before adding a suffix that begins with a vowel.  **Examples:** *bake* + *ing* = *baking, write* + *er* = *writer, slice* + *ing* = *slicing.*

**Add** *-ed* **and** *-ing* **to the base words.**

bake

rope

chase

hope

save

mope

taste

**Read each sentence.**
**Add the suffix _-ing_ to each word and complete the sentences correctly.**

## Word List

| hope | fly | save | take |
|------|-----|------|------|

1. Cara and her family are _____ a vacation this summer.

2. Cara is _____ her money so that she can buy some gifts there.

3. The family will be _____ on an airplane.

4. Cara is _____ that she will have a great time.

**3** **Write three sentences. Use at least three of the words from the list.**

1. _____

_____

_____

2. _____

_____

_____

3. _____

_____

**Word List**

taking

hoping

riding

hiding

saving

baking

## Definition:

Synonyms are words that mean the same or almost the same thing but are spelled differently.  Examples:  *big*/*large*, *small*/*little*, *closes*/*shuts*.

**1** Read each word.  Write its synonym on the line.

junk  _____

close  _____

sick  _____

| fast |
| ill |
| trash |
| happy |
| wet |
| shut |
| big |
| little |

large  _____

small  _____

glad  _____

damp  _____

**2** Read each sentence.
Think of a synonym for the word shown.  Write the synonym on the line.

1. Please _____ the door when you leave.
   close

2. Julie was _____ when she saw her friend.
   glad

3. The house is very _____ .
   large

4. He is a _____ runner.

5. Mary is feeling _____ today.
   ill

**Read the story.  Use the words from the list to complete the story.**

Sharon was going to ride in a race. She didn't know if

she would be _____ enough to win. There was a

_____ number of people in the race. She was

_____ when she saw that her friend Dan was in the

race also. Sharon knew the race would be _____ .

**Write four sentences.  Include words that are synonyms in each sentence.**

1. _____

_____

2. _____

_____

3. _____

_____

4. _____

_____

**1.** **Read each word.  Write its antonym next to it on the line.**

| | | |
|---|---|---|
| stop _____ | small | out _____ |
| | dry | |
| over _____ | in | awake _____ |
| | asleep | |
| big _____ | under | down _____ |
| | up | |
| full _____ | empty | wet _____ |
| | go | |

**2.** **Read each sentence.  Think of an antonym for the word shown.**
**Write the word on the line.**

1. The boy is _____ .
   awake

2. Jane is _____ .
   happy

3. He works in the _____ .
   night

4. The glass is _____ .
   empty

5. He is _____ .
   standing

**3** Use the words from the list to complete the crossword puzzle.

full

light

tall

frown

dark

**ACROSS:**

1. Antonym for smile.
2. Antonym for heavy.

**DOWN:**

1. Antonym for empty.
3. Antonym for short.

**4** Write a sentence for each of the following words:

Antonym of *hard*

Antonym of *start*

Antonym of *old*

Antonym of *long*

1. _____

2. _____

3. _____

4. _____

## Definition:

**Homonyms are words that sound the same but have different spellings and different meanings. Examples:** *beet*/*beat*, *weak*/*week*, *buy*/*by*.

**Read each word. Match each word with its homonym.**

weight _____

week _____

sew _____

heel _____

blew _____

pane _____

meat _____

sea _____

to _____

son _____

| |
|---|
| meet |
| see |
| pain |
| two |
| sun |
| heal |
| blue |
| wait |
| so |
| weak |

**Use the words from the list to complete the sentences.**

1. Dan can lift a lot of _____.

2. The ship sailed on the _____.

3. There are seven days in a _____.

4. After one comes _____.

5. My favorite color is _____.

6. Grandma likes to _____ clothes for me.

7. Sarah likes to _____ new people.

8. John had a blister on his _____.

9. The _____ of glass is broken.

10. The _____ is very hot today.

weight

wait

week

weak

sew

so

heel

heal

pane

pain

meet

meat

sea

see

to

two

son

sun

blew

blue

Write a short poem.

In this lesson you will write a poem using synonyms, antonyms, and homonyms. This poem should be about playing with a friend or a relative. You might want to look at some poetry books before you start.

Your poem should be at least five lines long. Have your teacher or writing partner help you to get some ideas going. He or she can also help you fix any mistakes in spelling or capitalization. Write your first copy on a piece of paper. Then write your final copy on the following page.

# What do you know ?

## Test 16
### Lessons 151–160
### 51 points

Name: _____

**1** Write the plural form for each word.

sheep _____     foot _____

deer _____     goose _____

child _____     tooth _____

man _____     mouse _____

**2** Write the possessive form of each word.

boy _____     girl _____

man _____     John _____

friend _____     teacher _____

**3** **Add** *-ing* **or** *-er* **to each word.  Some words may take more than one suffix.**

run _____     _____

dig _____     _____

plan _____     _____

sad _____     _____

fit _____     _____

**4** **Add** *-ed*, *-ing*, *-er*, **or** *-est* **to each word.  Some words may take more than one suffix.**

cute _____     _____

love _____     _____

come _____     _____

smile _____     _____

nice _____     _____

late _____     _____

*Horizons Phonics & Reading 1, Workbook Two*

**5** **Match each word with its *synonym*.**

large _____

small _____

| tidy |
| fast |
| wet |
| big |
| little |
| happy |

glad _____

neat _____

damp _____

**6** **Match each word with its *antonym*.**

hot _____

wet _____

weak _____

| down |
| empty |
| slow |
| dry |
| strong |
| cold |

full _____

fast _____

up _____

**7** **Match each word with its *homonym*.**

male _____

two _____

no _____

| blue |
| ate |
| to |
| pain |
| know |
| mail |

pane _____

eight _____

blew _____